GOING UP!

Contents

Dee Reid

Story illustrated by
Tom Percival

Heinemann

Find out about

- All kinds of special ladders

Tricky words

- uses
- firefighter
- rescue
- special
- coastguard
- salmon

Introduce these tricky words and help the reader when they come across them later!

Text starter

Lots of people use ladders but some people use special ladders. Firefighters and coastguards use special ladders to rescue people. But even a salmon and a budgie use special ladders.

All Kinds of Ladders

Who uses this ladder?

A firefighter uses this ladder to rescue people.

This is a special ladder.

Who uses this ladder?

A coastguard uses this ladder to rescue people.

This is a special ladder.

dam

ladder

Who uses this ladder?

A salmon uses this ladder to get to its home.

The salmon jumps up the steps of the ladder to get past the dam.

This is a special ladder.

Who uses this ladder?

A budgie uses this ladder
to get to its bell!

Quiz

Text Detective

- Which people need special ladders for their work?
- What have you learned about ladders that you did not know before?

Word Detective

- **Phonic Focus:** Initial phonemes

  Page 8: Find a word that starts with the phoneme 'g'.
- Page 9: Find the word 'this' twice.
- Page 9: Find a sentence that is a question.

Super Speller

Read this word:

a

Now try to spell it!

HA! HA! HA!

Q Why did the boy bring a ladder to school?

A Because he went to the high school!

Before Reading

In this story

 Rusty

 The man

 The lady

Tricky words

- ladder
- dangerous
- move
- stuck
- down

Introduce these tricky words and help the reader when they come across them later!

Story starter

Rusty is a robot. He is old and rusty but he likes to help people. One day, Rusty saw a ladder leaning against a shed. "That ladder is dangerous," said Rusty.

Rusty and the Ladder

"That ladder is dangerous," said Rusty.

"I can move the ladder," said Rusty.

"Help! Help!" said the man.
"I am stuck!"

Rusty put the ladder down.

What has Rusty done wrong?

"Help! Help!" said the lady.
"I am stuck!"

"You rusty tin can,"
said the man.
"Put the ladder back!"

"Help! Help!" said the man.

"Help! Help!" said the lady.

"I can help you," said Rusty.

Quiz

Text Detective

- Why did Rusty move the ladder?
- Was it fair of the man to be cross with Rusty?

Word Detective

- **Phonic Focus:** Initial phonemes

  Page 18: Find a word beginning with the phoneme 'b'.
- Page 16: Find a word that means the opposite of 'up'.
- Page 17: Find two capital letters.

Super Speller

Read this word:

I

Now try to spell it!

HA! **HA!** **HA!**

Q What's got a bottom at the top?

A A leg.